GREAT MINDS® WIT & WISDOM

Grade 4 Module 4:
Myth Making

Student Edition

Table of Contents

Handout 23A: Fluency Homework

Handout 24A: Story within a Story Map, Part 2

Handout 25A: Poems in *Walk Two Moons*

Handout 25B: "The Tide Rises, The Tide Falls"

Handout 25C: Themes/Messages/Lessons

Handout 26A: Evidence Organizer for Focusing Question Task 4

Handout 27A: Formal vs. Informal English

Handout 28A: Fluency Homework

Handout 28B: Frederick/Fredericka and Freddy/Franny

Handout 30A: Norms for Speaking Collaboratively

Handout 30B: Ways to Participate in a Collaborative Conversation

Handout 31A: Informative/Explanatory Writing Checklist

Handout 32A: Evidence Organizer for End-of-Module Task

Handout 33A: Speaking and Listening Checklist

Handout 34A: End-of-Module Task Essay Planner

Handout 35A: Informative/Explanatory Writing Checklist

Handout 36A: Greatest Heart Nominee

Volume of Reading Reflection Questions

Wit & Wisdom Parent Tip Sheet

Name: _____

Date: _____

Handout 2A: Exit Ticket

Directions: Write three characteristics of myths, the names of two Greek gods/goddesses, and one way Greeks honored their gods.

_____

_____

_____

_____

_____

_____

_____

Name: _____

Date: _____

Handout 2B: Evidence Paragraphs

Directions: Examine the two example paragraphs to determine which one uses evidence most effectively.

- Read each of the paragraphs, looking for how the author used evidence in each paragraph.
- Underline text evidence that you find.

Evidence Paragraph 1

A myth is a story that is told over and over and explains why something is the way it is. The ancient Greeks had many myths they shared about all the gods they believed in. The ancient Greeks created myths to teach people why natural events happened and to tell their people how to behave. Myths help us understand what the ancient Greeks believed long ago. Their myths were told over and over to spread their beliefs and shape how people behaved.

Evidence Paragraph 2

A myth is a story that is told over and over and explains why something is the way it is. The ancient Greeks had many myths they shared about all the gods they believed in. The ancient Greeks created myths to teach people why natural events happened and to tell their people how to behave. Creation myths explained everything in nature. The myth about Demeter explains why we have seasons. Demeter was sad when her daughter was stolen away by Hades to the underworld. Because she was sad, Demeter stopped caring for the crops, and they died. This explained winter. Greeks had morality myths, too, which taught people how to behave. For example, the myth about Arachne explains that someone who is boastful and disrespectful will be punished. Arachne disrespected the goddess Athena and was turned into a spider as a punishment. This myth explains what will happen if you behave badly and explains why there are spiders in the world. Myths help us understand what the ancient Greeks believed long ago. Their myths were told over and over to spread their beliefs and shape how people behaved.

Name: _____

Date: _____

Handout 2C: Fluency Homework

Directions:

1. Day 1: Read the text carefully and annotate to help you read fluently.
2. Each day:
   a. Practice reading the text aloud three to five times.
   b. Evaluate your progress by placing a checkmark in the appropriate, unshaded box.
   c. Ask someone (adult or peer) to listen and evaluate you as well.
3. Last day: Answer the self-reflection question at the end.

But when the battle of Troy broke out and Achilles went to fight, the very thing his mother had tried to prevent happened: during a siege on the city, one fateful arrow pierced his heel, his only mortal part, killing him.

Still, Achilles became revered as one of the greatest Greek heroes, for without him, the Greeks never would have defeated the Trojans. He lives on in our language also. We call a person's weakness his or her *Achilles' heel*, especially if that person seems otherwise invincible.

Lunge-Larsen, Lise. *Gifts from the Gods: Ancient Words & Wisdom from Greek & Roman Mythology*. Illustrated by Gareth Hinds, Houghton Mifflin Harcourt, 2011, pp. 4–5.

Student Performance Checklist:	Day 1		Day 2		Day 3		Day 4	
	You	Listener*	You	Listener*	You	Listener*	You	Listener*
Accurately read the passage three to five times.								
Read with appropriate phrasing and pausing.								

Read with appropriate expression.								
Read articulately at a good pace and an audible volume.								

*Adult or peer

Self-reflection: What choices did you make when deciding how to read this passage, and why? What would you like to improve on or try differently next time? (Thoughtfully answer these questions in the space below. Use a separate sheet of paper if necessary to complete your reflection.)

Name: _____

Date: _____

Handout 3A: "Pandora's Box" Organizer

Directions:

- Read the myth, "Pandora's Box," in *Gifts from the Gods: Ancient Words & Wisdom from Greek & Roman Mythology.*
- Record answers to the questions about the myth in the boxes on the left.
- Read pages 10–15 in *Understanding Greek Myths.*
- Record details from the text that support your answers about "Pandora's Box."

1. What role did the gods play?

"Pandora's Box"	*Understanding Greek Myths*

2. What was the problem?

"Pandora's Box"	Understanding Greek Myths

3. How was the problem resolved?

"Pandora's Box"	Understanding Greek Myths

Name: _____

Date: _____

4. What idea does this myth explain?

"Pandora's Box"	Understanding Greek Myths

5. What can we learn about the beliefs of the ancient Greeks? How does the myth relate to the word *moral*?

"Pandora's Box"	Understanding Greek Myths

Name: _____

Date: _____

4. What idea does this myth explain?

"Pandora's Box"	Understanding Greek Myths

5. What can we learn about the beliefs of the ancient Greeks? How does the myth relate to the word *moral*?

"Pandora's Box"	Understanding Greek Myths

Name: _____

Date: _____

Handout 3B: Evidence Organizer

Directions: Choose the strongest evidence to support your focus statement. Write brief notes in the boxes. Follow the prompts at the top of the chart. Remember to only write notes that support your focus statement.

Prompt: For an audience who might be interested in learning more about myths and why people created them, write a well-developed paragraph in which you explain what a myth is and why the Greeks created them. Develop your ideas with evidence and examples from pages 6–23 of *Understanding Greek Myths* and from the book *Gifts from the Gods*.

Focus Statement:

Context	Evidence	Source	Elaboration/Explanation
	List details from the text that support your focus statement. Be sure to use quotations and paraphrasing.	Where did this information come from? List title and page number.	Why is this important? What does this help us understand?
What are the characteristics of myths?			
Include gods and goddesses.			

Context	Evidence	Source	Elaboration/Explanation
What are the characteristics of myths?	**List details from the text that support your focus statement. Be sure to use quotations and paraphrasing.**	**Where did this information come from? List title and page number.**	**Why is this important? What does this help us understand?**
Include heroes and monsters.			
Creation myths tell how the world came to be.			
Morality myths taught people how to behave.			

Name: _____

Date: _____

Handout 3C: "Pandora's Box" Glossary

Directions: Use this glossary to understand the meanings of some of the words in the story of "Pandora's Box" in *Gifts from the Gods: Ancient Words & Wisdom from Greek & Roman Mythology.*

Word	Definition	Example
infused	Mixed together.	The athlete's talent was <u>infused</u> with strength and skill.
insatiable	Can't be satisfied or fulfilled.	The bear had an <u>insatiable</u> hunger for fish.
bestowed	To be given something.	The child was <u>bestowed</u> with special gifts on her birthday.
quarrel	To fight or argue.	The kids had a <u>quarrel</u> about who would be the team captains.
endure	To work through, or deal with, a difficult challenge or event.	She <u>endured</u> the difficult math homework because she knew it would help her on her test.

Name: _____

Date: _____

Handout 3D: Morphology Flashcards

Directions: Cut out the cards and shuffle them. Match each word to its definition.

monochrome	having one color
polychrome	having many colors
monocle	eyeglass for one eye
monologue	a long speech given by one person
monopoly	when one company controls most of a product or service
polygon	a shape with many angles
apathy	without feelings about something
amoral	without morals
abyss	without a bottom like a bottomless pit
theology	the study of god or gods

Name: _____

Date: _____

Handout 4A: Myth Analyzer

Directions: Reread the myth about Victoria in *Gifts from the Gods*. Record bulleted notes to answer each guiding question.

What is happening?	What mystery does this myth solve?

What are the themes?	Where do we see aspects of this myth today?

Name: _____

Date: _____

Handout 4B: Frequently Confused Words

Directions: Refer to the chart to write in the correct words in the sentences below.

to	Indicates a preposition: Go <u>to</u> the store.
two	The number 2: Please give me <u>two</u> pennies.
too	The word *also* could replace it: I want to see, <u>too</u>. OR An excess of: It is taking <u>too</u> much time.
there	Location: The water is over <u>there</u>.
their	Ownership: <u>Their</u> car broke down.
its	A pronoun: The tree lost <u>its</u> leaves.
it's	A contraction meaning *it is*: <u>It's</u> cold out today.

1. Please give me _____ new address so I can send a holiday card.

2. There were _____ roosters in the road this morning.

3. If you go to the fair, I would like to go, _____.

4. We went _____ school at 8:00 in the morning.

5. _____ is a new secretary in the front office.

6. The moon lit up the night sky with _____ glow.

7. I am glad that _____ almost the weekend.

Name: _____

Date: _____

Handout 5A: Myth Presentations Notes

Directions: Record brief notes about each myth as groups present their posters.

Title of Myth	Creation Myth or Morality Myth? Explain.	Theme	Vocabulary
Arachne			
Grace			
Demeter and Persephone			

Title of Myth	Creation Myth or Morality Myth? Explain.	Theme	Vocabulary
Prometheus			
Heracles			
Echo and Narcissus			

Name: _____

Date: _____

Handout 6A: Greek Myth Title Cards

Directions: Cut out the cards along the dotted lines.

Demeter and Persephone	Victory
Arachne	Achilles' Heel
Echo and Narcissus	Prometheus
Pandora's Box	Heracles
Grace	

Name:

Date:

Handout 6B: Theme Strips

Directions: Cut out the strips along the dotted lines.

Life versus death

Justice will win

How evils and hope entered the world

Hard work is rewarded

Why we have seasons

How spiders came into the world

How people got fire

You will be punished if you disrespect the gods

Being full of yourself will be punished

There are consequences for disobeying a god

Why some people are generous and kind

Name: _____

Date: _____

Handout 6C: Editing Sentences

Directions: Use the anchor chart for Frequently Confused Words and a dictionary to proofread the following sentences. Cross out the word in error and write the correct spelling above the word.

1. A German archelogest set out too find the roons of the city of Troy.

2. They hid there bravest soldyers inside the hoarse.

3. The peeple had no king, but the oracle said that there king would arrive by oxcart.

4. The temples that the Greeks built for there gods were carefuly balanced in size and shap.

5. Although they got the idea two write things down from there tradeing partners, the Greeks added simbols for vowels.

Sentences adapted from *Understanding Greek Myths* by Natalie Hyde

Name: _____

Date: _____

Handout 6D: Editing a Paragraph

Directions: Proofread the following paragraph by circling misspelled words or incorrectly used words. Use the anchor chart and a dictionary to check spelling if necessary. Write the revised words above the incorrect words.

In the country of Greece there lived a goddess named Fortuna. She brought good fortune

two many people. They were happy for there fortunes from her. If she carried a ball, she

was concerned with luck. If she carried a horn of plenty they're were riches too be found.

Soldiers, sailors, farmers, and all who depended on luck prayed to Fortuna. There prayers

two Fortuna were supposed too protect them. One day she ignored there pleas for help and

they're ships sank. However, she always favored those who were bold and brave.

Sentences adapted from *Gifts from the Gods* by Lise Lunge-Larsen.

Name: _____

Date: _____

Handout 7A: Informative/Explanatory Writing Checklist

Directions: Use this checklist to revise your writing. Mark **+** for "yes" and Δ for "not yet." Ask someone (adult or peer) to evaluate your writing as well.

Reading Comprehension	Self +/Δ	Peer +/Δ	Teacher +/Δ
Describe what a myth is.			
Explain why ancient Greeks created myths.			
Use text evidence to support your explanations.			
Structure			
I respond to all parts of the prompt.			
I focus on my topic throughout my paragraph.			
I introduce the topic clearly with a topic sentence.			
I group similar ideas together in my paragraph.			
My conclusion sentence relates to my explanation.			
I use transitions to link ideas.			
Development			
I develop my topic with evidence from text(s).			
My evidence is related to the topic.			
I elaborate upon evidence by explaining or analyzing it.			
Style			
I use a variety of sentence patterns (simple, compound, complex).			
I use vocabulary words that are specific and appropriate to the content.			
My writing style is appropriate for the audience.			

Conventions			
I underline two frequently confused words to show I have used them correctly.			
Writing Process			
I revise my paragraph to improve my ideas.			
I revise my paragraph to improve my word choice.			
I edit my paragraph for correct spelling.			
I edit my paragraph for correct punctuation.			
I edit my paragraph for correct capitalization.			
Total number of +'s			

Name: _____

Date: _____

Handout 8A: Fluency Homework

Directions:

1. Day 1: Read the text carefully and annotate to help you read fluently.
2. Each day:
   a. Practice reading the text aloud three to five times.
   b. Evaluate your progress by placing a check mark in the appropriate, unshaded box.
   c. Ask someone (adult or peer) to listen and evaluate you as well.
3. Last day: Answer the self-reflection question at the end.

Scene 1: A Village on the Northwest Coast

The people of the village pantomime various activities such as carving wood, fixing fishing nets, working on canoes, and mixing food. Raven stands in his tree to one side of the stage.

RAVEN: Caa-awk, Caa-awk. My name is Raven. One of my jobs is to keep watch. That's why you see me on top of the tallest trees like this one. I can see better up here. Let me tell you a story about something I saw once long ago. It's a good story. It's about a monster and some brave people. It's a story about me too. Caa-awk, Caa-awk! That makes the story even better.

VILLAGE CHIEF: What a good day this is. I am glad we moved to this village.

FIRST MAN: I just hope that cannibal monster does not find us again.

Bruchac, Joseph. *Pushing Up the Sky: Seven Native American Plays for Children*. Illustrated by Teresa Flavin. Dial Books for Young Readers, 2000, p. 70.

Student Performance Checklist:	Day 1		Day 2		Day 3		Day 4	
	You	Listener*	You	Listener*	You	Listener*	You	Listener*
Accurately read the passage three to five times.								
Read with appropriate phrasing and pausing.								
Read with appropriate expression.								
Read articulately at a good pace and an audible volume.								

*Adult or peer

Self-reflection: What choices did you make when deciding how to read this passage, and why? What would you like to improve on or try differently next time? (Thoughtfully answer these questions in the space below. Use a separate sheet of paper if necessary to complete your reflection.)

Name: _____

Date: _____

Handout 9A: Drama Organizer

Directions: Use this chart to organize and record notes about key details in the play "Gluskabe and Old Man Winter."

Character(s):	Setting:

Conflict(s):
The main problem in this part of the story is...

Resolution:

Summary:

Theme:

Directions: Write an introduction for the play that includes the following:
- What the reader will learn by reading the play.
- Background information to understand the play.
- Specific words and phrases to make the reader want to continue reading.

_____

_____

_____

_____

_____

_____

_____

_____

_____

_____

_____

Name: _____

Date: _____

Handout 10A: Evidence Organizer

Directions: Choose the best evidence to support your focus statement. Write brief notes in the boxes. Follow the prompts at the top of the chart. Remember to only write notes that support your focus statement.

Prompt: What do myths from different cultures have in common?

Focus Statement:

Context	Evidence	Source	Elaboration/Explanation	
What is the name and theme of the myth?	List details from the text that support your focus statement. Be sure to use quotations and paraphrasing.	Where did this information come from? List title and page number.	What does this help us understand?	

Prompt: What do myths from different cultures have in common?

Focus Statement:

Context	Evidence	Source	Elaboration/Explanation
What is the name and theme of the myth?	List details from the text that support your focus statement. Be sure to use quotations and paraphrasing.	Where did this information come from? List title and page number.	What does this help us understand?
Similarities in theme and importance			

Name: _____

Date: _____

Handout 11A: Introduction Template

Directions: Fill in the boxes with complete, detailed sentences to write an introduction for a compare/contrast essay about two myths from different cultures.

Hook	
Identify and describe myth 1	
Identify and describe myth 2	
Focus Statement (Thesis that tells how the myths are similar in theme)	

Helpful Tool

Sentence Frame for Thesis:

_____ and _____ are similar

because _____.

Name: _____

Date: _____

Handout 12A: Guiding Questions to Analyze Myths

Directions: Use the questions below to guide your discussion about each myth. Record your ideas on a new copy of Handout 11A: Evidence Organizer.

Steps to Analyze a Story	Questions to Ask
Summarize the Story	• What was the problem the people faced? • How did they try to solve the problem? Was it successful or not? • What was the next problem the people faced? • How did they try to solve it? Was it successful or not? • How did the story end?
Determine the Theme of the Story	• What is the lesson taught? • What is explained by the story?
Why Does This Matter?	• What do these stories reveal to us about the challenges people face? • Are the people in the stories more similar or different in how they behave? Why? • If the people who told these stories never met, how is it possible that the lessons they teach are so similar? • What does this teach us about being human?

Name: _____

Date: _____

Handout 12B: Other Native American Tales

Directions: Read one of the myths and complete an evidence organizer to explain how the theme of the myth compares to another myth from a different culture.

The Sun, Moon, and Stars

A traditional Navajo story retold by Donna Henes

The First People had only four lights to illuminate the world: white light from the eastern mountains, blue light from the southern mountains, yellow light from the western peaks, and darkness from the north. These lights were dim and much too far away to bring heat.

The people wanted more daylight. "We barely have enough to see," they complained.

So First Woman sent Glowworm, Fox Fire, Lightning Beetle, and Firefly to the four corners. They would give more light when it was needed.

But the First People were still not satisfied. "These lights are too small. They flicker on and off and are of little use to us. We do not have night eyes like Owl or Bat!"

First Woman kept trying to please her people. She consulted Fire Man on his glowing mountain. He offered to make the land around Fire Mountain bright, but he warned her that the light would not cover all the lands and there would be smoke.

The people liked the brightness, but they were still not happy. "We do not like the heat and the smoke that comes from Fire Mountain. The heat scorches the earth and we are choked by the smoke," they grumbled.

Eventually, First Woman had an idea for a different way to send light to Earth. She asked for a large, flat piece of the hardest rock available. After a long search, the people brought her a slab of quartz. It took a lot of hard work and a lot of help for First Woman to carve the quartz into two wheels.

Once the wheels were ready, First Woman and First Man decorated them as faces with symbols of the powers they each had. They decorated the first wheel with a mask of blue turquoise to give light and heat. They attached red coral to the earlobes and around the rim. On each side was a horn to hold male lightning and rain. On the rim, they placed bird feathers—cardinal, lark, and eagle—to fly it through the sky and spread the rays of heat and light in the four directions. This was the Sun wheel.

When it was time to decorate the second wheel, First Woman said, "We do not need more heat and light. This one will carry coolness and moisture." She and First Man used white shell to create a face, with a band of yellow pollen on its chin and a rim of red coral. This wheel had feathers, too: magpie, nighthawk, turkey, and crane feathers to bear its weight. Its horns held female lightning and soft winds. This was Moon wheel.

"This Sun wheel and Moon wheel cannot stay here," declared First Woman. "We must place them in the sky!" First Man suggested they carry the disks to the top of the highest mountain and fasten them to the sky with darts of lightning, which the people did.

Now the people had light, heat, coolness, and moisture all coming from the sky. But still they found something to complain about. Because the Sun always stayed in the east and never moved, one side of the land had an unending summer, and the other side had a winter that lasted forever. "This is not right," they whined.

First Man agreed. "The Sun must move across the sky, but how can it travel when it is only a stone and has no spirit?" At that moment, two ancient, wise men stepped forward and offered to help. "We will give our spirits to the Sun and the Moon so they will have life and power to move across the sky." One entered the turquoise disk and he was called Jóhonaa'áí, or Sun Bearer; the other entered the white disk and he was called Tl'éhonaa'áí, or Moon Bearer.

Once the Sun and the Moon were following their paths through the sky, the people returned to where First Woman had carved the wheels. The blanket where she had worked was covered with many small stone chips of every shape and size, plus stone dust from the cutting.

"These white stones must not be wasted! We will use them to make more lights in the night sky," exclaimed First Woman. So again, they worked with their flint knives, chisels, and stone hammers to shape the stars.

To this day, the Sun, the Moon, and the stars created by First Woman, First Man, and all the people remain in the sky where they give light and heat by day and luminous, sparkling patterns at night.

"The Sun, Moon, and Stars." Retold by Donna Henes, *Appleseeds*, Jan. 2007. *Cricket Media,* Carus Publishing Company.

Legend of the Moccasin Flower
An Ojibwe Tale retold by Mary Morton Cowan

For many moons, in the woods near Kitchigami (kit-chee-GAH-mee, Lake Superior), the Ojibwe stripped birch bark and cut limbs to make wigwams and canoes. They fished in the big lake and harvested wild rice and corn. They gathered sarsaparilla, mugwort, and other herbs to use for healing the sick. During Lake-Freezing Moon (November), they hunted for deer, moose, and bear.

One winter, during Gitci-manito-gizis (gi-chee-MAN-i-toe-gee-zis), (Big Spirit Moon), a terrible sickness swept through an Ojibwe village. People burned sage and cedar boughs in their wigwams to purify the air. The mide (medicine man) chanted songs to attract healing spirits to each wigwam. He sprinkled boiled solomon-seal root on hot stones for the sick to inhale healing fumes. Yet, one after another, people died. Before long, all the medicinal herbs were gone.

The chief summoned a young messenger boy. "Running Wolf," the chief said, "you must hurry to the next village. We need mucki-ki (healing herbs) to save the rest of our people." But Running Wolf also became ill. His body began to burn with the dreaded fever, and he could not get up from his mat. White Rabbit, his young sister, became frightened.

"I will fetch the healing herbs," she said. "No," said Running Wolf. "You cannot survive this bitter cold. It is a long distance to the next village, and the way is dangerous. It must be the wish of Kitche Manitou (KIT-chee MAN-i-too), the Great Spirit, that all our village shall die." White Rabbit could not bear to see her brother die. Already many of their family and neighbors had perished. She could not let any more villagers suffer this terrible sickness. Even during this frigid moon, she must get help for her people.

While Running Wolf slept by the fire, White Rabbit found the deerskin moccasins she had helped her mother sew and lined them with rabbit fur. She thought about the dangerous journey. With her mother and the other women of the village, she had harvested berries. She had harvested wild rice in the swamp and reeds for rush mats. Surely, she could find her way to the next village.

Wrapping her fur coat about her, and wearing her beaver mittens, she slipped through the doorway of the wigwam into the howling winter wind. Snow stung her face. She shivered with cold, but kept trudging through the snow. When night fell over the valley, White Rabbit imagined frightening spirits chasing her, screeching with the winds through the blackness. She crossed the icy swamp and finally saw a glimmer of firelight from the neighboring village.

White Rabbit was welcomed into a wigwam, where she told her story. "Please, I need a bundle of mucki-ki to help my village," she said. "Many people are dying of a terrible sickness."

"Here, I have a pouch of yarrow and goldenrod, sumac, and tamarack root," said an old woman. "At daybreak, a messenger will go with you. Now, my child, warm yourself by this fire."

After eating a bowl of berries and boiled rice, White Rabbit snuggled under the woman's moosehide blanket. But she could not wait until morning. Without the herbs, Running Wolf and the others would soon die. After the old woman had fallen asleep, White Rabbit crept out into the cold, carrying the pouch of medicinal herbs. She darted across the snowfields and through the icy swamp. Trees creaked and groaned. It was so cold, one tree cracked

Name: _____

Date: _____

with a thunderous clap, just as she ran by. It frightened her so, she did not notice her moccasins had come off until she was well beyond the spot.

"Oh dear," she cried. "I cannot go back. There is not enough time to find my moccasins. They are buried deep in snow by now."

Weary, she ran on, clutching the medicine. The crusty snow cut her bare feet. Just before dawn, she reached the edge of the forest. Her cracked, bleeding feet were so painful that she could walk no farther. Almost home, she fell in the snow.

"Help!" she cried out. "I have come with mucki-ki!"

Villagers came running. They carried White Rabbit into the wigwam and covered her with fur robes, wrapping her frostbitten feet to warm them. The herbs healed the people, and there were no more deaths in the village that winter. Next spring, during Flowering Moon, White Rabbit and Running Wolf discovered beautiful new flowers in the woods. Each delicate blossom was shaped like a tiny moccasin, pink and white.

"This is where I lost my moccasins in the deep snow," said White Rabbit.

Thereafter White Rabbit was called Wah-onnay, "Little Flower." Today many moons later, this precious moccasin flower is commonly called the lady's slipper. It grows in the woods of Kitchigami Land and beyond – a delicate reminder of a brave Ojibwe maiden.

"Legend of the Moccasin Flower: An Ojibwe Tale." Retold by Mary Morton Cowan, *Faces*, April 2010. *Cricket Media*, Carus Publishing Company.

Name: _____

Date: _____

Handout 12C: Evidence Organizer

Directions: Choose the best evidence to support your focus statement. Write brief notes in the boxes. Follow the prompts at the top of the chart. Remember to only write notes that support your focus statement.

Prompt: What do myths from different cultures have in common?

Focus Statement:

Context	Evidence	Source	Elaboration/Explanation
What is the name and theme of the myth?	List details from the text that support your focus statement. Be sure to use quotations and paraphrasing.	Where did this information come from? List title and page number.	What does this help us understand?

Prompt: What do myths from different cultures have in common?

Focus Statement:

Context	Evidence	Source	Elaboration/Explanation
What is the name and theme of the myth?	List details from the text that support your focus statement. Be sure to use quotations and paraphrasing.	Where did this information come from? List title and page number.	What does this help us understand?
Similarities in theme and importance			

Name: _____

Date: _____

Handout 12D: Introduction Template

Directions: Fill in the boxes with complete, detailed sentences to write an introduction for a compare/contrast essay about two myths from different cultures.

Hook	
Identify and describe myth 1.	
Identify and describe myth 2.	
Focus Statement (Thesis that tells how the myths are similar in theme)	

Helpful Tool

Sentence Frame for Thesis:

_____ and _____ are similar

because _____.

Name:

Date:

Handout 14A: "When Raven Soared"

Directions: Read the text carefully, then refer to it as needed to answer the questions on Assessment 14A: New-Read Assessment 1.

"When Raven Soared," Leigh Anderson ("A trickster myth . . .")

Long ago—when the Earth was young and unsettled—humans were not always humans, and animals were not always animals. Magic wove its way into the air. Raven soared over treeless frozen tundra, snowcapped mountains, and towering pine trees. He rode through icy waters on the backs of whales. On land, he walked among the people, wearing a feathered cape.

Raven was a trickster and mischief-maker who took on many forms—from a prancing deer to a cedar splinter. He was as vain as he was wise. He was as boastful as he was big-hearted. Often, he lied or misled others and fell into sticky messes of his own making. Raven made mistakes, but he had great power and spirit. He tried to do what was right—most of the time.

When Raven saw the people struggling in darkness, he decided to help. A greedy, powerful chief had stolen the stars, Moon, and Sun. He had trapped them in three beautiful boxes, letting no one near their light. But Raven knew the greedy Chief's greatest wish: a grandson. With this knowledge, Raven made a plan.

One day, Raven saw the Chief's daughter drinking from a creek. He turned himself into a pine needle and floated on the water. The girl swallowed this pine needle as she drank. Some months later, the Chief's daughter had a baby boy. The boy grew quickly and made the Chief proud. But the boy was really Raven.

One day, the boy (who was Raven) pointed to one of three beautifully carved boxes. "Ga-a! Ga-a!" he cried, until the Chief let him play with the box. When the Chief looked away, Raven opened the box and let out the stars.

When the Chief lost his anger, Raven asked for the second beautifully carved box. "Ga-a! Ga-a!" he cried again, until the Chief let him play with the box. When the Chief looked away, Raven opened the box and out flew the Moon.

When the Chief lost his anger, Raven asked for the last beautifully carved box. "Ga-a! Ga-a!" he cried a third time, until the Chief let him play with the box. When the Chief looked away, Raven opened the box and a golden ball of light rolled out.

Raven turned back into a bird and flew up through the lodge's smoke-hole. He tossed the Sun into the sky and soared away into the clouds. The great Chief shook his fists and shouted with anger. But Raven only cawed and cackled as the Sun warmed his feathers and gave light to the people of the world.

So say the legends of the people who first settled the Pacific Northwest coast. Their languages and stories are often as different as the places in which they live, but Raven flies through many of their myths. He shows us humanity's worst and best qualities. We may not always make the right choices, but—if our hearts are in the right place—we can make things come out for the best in the end.

Other Native American myths have "trickster" characters, too. Coyote slinks through many of the Great Plains tribal legends. Hare bounds through southeastern native tales. Blue Jay has top-flight billing in many eastern-forest tribal myths.

Anderson, Leigh. "When Raven Soared." *Appleseeds*, Mar. 2008. *Cricket Media*, Carus Publishing Company.

Name: _____

Date: _____

Handout 14B: Informative/Explanatory Writing Checklist

Directions: Use this checklist to revise your writing. Mark **+** for "yes" and Δ for "not yet." Ask someone (adult or peer) to evaluate your writing as well.

Reading Comprehension	Self +/Δ	Peer +/Δ	Teacher +/Δ
Describe one myth or tale including its theme.			
Describe the other myth or tale including its theme.			
Explain similarities in treatment of theme.			
Explain why this matters.			
Structure			
I respond to all parts of the prompt.			
I focus on my topic throughout the piece.			
I introduce the topic clearly in my introduction paragraph.			
I organize my ideas into body paragraphs.			
My conclusion paragraph relates to my explanation.			
I use transitions to link paragraphs and ideas.			
Development			
I develop my topic with evidence from text(s).			
My evidence is related to the topic.			
I elaborate upon evidence by explaining or analyzing it.			
Style			
I use a variety of sentence patterns (simple, compound, complex).			
I use vocabulary words that are specific and appropriate to the content.			

My writing style is appropriate for the audience.			
Conventions			
I use two modal auxiliaries (can, may, must). Underline them.			
Writing Process			
I revise my essay to improve my ideas.			
I revise my essay to improve my word choice.			
I edit my essay for correct spelling.			
I edit my essay for correct punctuation.			
I edit my essay for correct capitalization.			
Total number of +'s			

Name: _____

Date: _____

Handout 15A: Fluency Homework

Directions:
1. Day 1: Read the text carefully and annotate to help you read fluently.
2. Each day:
   a. Practice reading the text aloud three to five times.
   b. Evaluate your progress by placing a checkmark in the appropriate, unshaded box.
   c. Ask someone (adult or peer) to listen and evaluate you as well.
3. Last day: Answer the self-reflection questions at the end.

Not long ago, when I was locked in a car with my grandparents for six days, I told them the story of Phoebe, and when I finished telling them—or maybe even as I was telling them—I realized that the story of Phoebe was like the plaster wall in our house in Bybanks, Kentucky.

My father started chipping away at a plaster wall in the living room of our house in Bybanks shortly after my mother left us one April morning. Our house was an old farmhouse that my parents had been restoring, room by room. Each night as he wanted to hear from my mother, he chipped away at that wall.

On the night that we got the bad news—that she was not returning—he pounded and pounded on that wall with a chisel and a hammer. At two o'clock in the morning, he came up to my room. I was not asleep. He led me downstairs and showed me what he had found. Hidden behind the wall was a brick fireplace.

The reason that Phoebe's story reminds me of that plaster wall and the hidden fireplace is that beneath Phoebe's story was another one. Mine.

Creech, Sharon. *Walk Two Moons*. 1994. HarperCollins, 2011.

Student Performance Checklist:	Day 1		Day 2		Day 3		Day 4	
	You	Listener*	You	Listener*	You	Listener*	You	Listener*
Accurately read the passage three to five times.								
Read with appropriate phrasing and pausing.								
Read with appropriate expression.								
Read articulately at a good pace, and an audible volume.								

*Adult or peer

Self-reflection: What choices did you make when deciding how to read this passage, and why? What would you like to improve on or try differently next time? (Thoughtfully answer these questions in the space below. Use a separate sheet of paper if necessary to complete your reflection.)

Name: _____

Date: _____

Handout 16A: Beginning Story Map

Directions: Record the story elements of *Walk Two Moons* in the three sections of the story map.

Characters	Settings
	Plot

Name: _____

Date: _____

Handout 16B: Evidence Organizer for Focusing Question Task 3

Directions: Choose the best evidence from *Walk Two Moons* to support your focus statement. Write brief notes in the boxes, and include linking words in your elaboration. Remember to only write notes that support your focus statement. Be sure to include the main connection.

Prompt: How are Sal's and Phoebe's stories connected?

Focus Statement: Sal and Phoebe are connected **because** they have many things in common, **and** they also share some similar experiences.

Context	Evidence	Source	Elaboration/Explanation
Things Sal and Phoebe have in common, or experiences they share	List details from the text that support your focus statement. Be sure to use quotations and paraphrasing.	Where did you find this information? List chapter and page number.	Explain or give more information about the quotations.
Connection 1			
Connection 2			
Connection 3			

Connection 4	Connection 5	Connection 6	Connection 7	Connection 8	Connection 9

Name: _____

Date: _____

Connection 10	Connection 11	Connection 12	Connection 13

Name: _____

Date: _____

Handout 16C: Prefix *fore-*

Part 1: Building Meaning

Directions: Build meanings with the prefix *fore-*. First, underline the root of each word (the part that is not the prefix). Then, try to build meaning without using a dictionary. If needed, use a dictionary to find the meaning of the word. See sample below.

1. Fore<u>shadow</u>: A writing device used to give a little bit of information ahead of time, and to hint at something to come.

2. Forearm:

3. Foreword:

4. Forerunner:

5. Forethought:

6. Foresee:

Part 2: Use a word with the prefix *fore-* in two sentences about *Walk Two Moons*.

1. _____

_____

2. _____

_____

Name: _____

Date: _____

Handout 17A: Story within a Story Map, Part 1

Directions: Record the main events under each category of each story in *Walk Two Moons*.

Sal's Memories of Kentucky	Phoebe's Story in Ohio	Sal's Journey to Idaho

Sal's Memories of Kentucky	Phoebe's Story in Ohio	Sal's Journey to Idaho

Name: _____

Date: _____

Handout 18A: Reactions/Reveals Chart

Directions: Write details from chapters 9–12 in the Reactions column about how each character reacts to the messages on Phoebe's porch. Think about what these details reveal about the character, and write some notes in the Reveals column about each character.

Character	Reactions	Reveals...
Mrs. Winterbottom		
Mr. Winterbottom		
Mary Lou		
Phoebe		
Sal		

Character	Reactions	Reveals...
Sal's father		
Ben		
Gram		

Name: _____

Date: _____

Handout 19A: Fluency Homework

Directions:

1. Day 1: Read the text carefully and annotate to help you read fluently.
2. Each day:
   a. Practice reading the text aloud three to five times.
   b. Evaluate your progress by placing a checkmark in the appropriate, unshaded box.
   c. Ask someone (adult or peer) to listen and evaluate you as well.
3. Last day: Answer the self-reflection questions at the end.

I wondered why it was so easy for me to see that Phoebe's mother was worried and miserable, but Phoebe couldn't see it–or if she could, she was ignoring it. Maybe she didn't *want* to notice. Maybe it was too frightening a thing. I wondered if this was how it had been with my mother. Were there things I didn't notice?

Later that afternoon, when Phoebe and I went downstairs, Mrs. Winterbottom was talking with Prudence. "Do you think I lead a tiny life?" she asked.

"How do you mean?" Prudence said, as she filed her nails. "Do we have any nail polish remover?"

Phoebe's mother retrieved a bottle of nail polish remover from the bathroom.

"Oh!" Prudence said. "Before I forget–do you think you could sew up the hem on my brown skirt so I could wear it tomorrow? Oh, please?" Prudence tilted her head to the side, tugged at her hair in exactly the same way Phoebe does, and smooshed up her mouth into a little pout.

"Doesn't Prudence know how to sew?" I asked.

"Of course she does," Phoebe said. "Why?"

"I was just wondering why she doesn't sew her own skirt."

"Sal, you're becoming very critical."

Before I left Phoebe's that day, Mrs. Winterbottom handed Prudence her brown skirt with the newly sewn hem, and all the way home I wondered about Mrs. Winterbottom and what she meant about living a tiny life. If she didn't like all that baking and cleaning and jumping up to get bottles of nail polish remover and sewing hems, shy did she do it? Why didn't she tell them to do some of these things themselves? Maybe she was afraid there would be nothing left for her to do. There would be no need for her and she would become invisible and no one would notice.

Creech, Sharon. *Walk Two Moons*. 1994. HarperCollins, 2011.

Student Performance Checklist:	Day 1		Day 2		Day 3		Day 4	
	You	Listener*	You	Listener*	You	Listener*	You	Listener*
Accurately read the passage three to five times.								
Read with appropriate phrasing and pausing.								
Read with appropriate expression.								
Read articulately at a good pace, and an audible volume.								

*Adult or peer

Self-reflection: What choices did you make when deciding how to read this passage, and why? What would you like to improve on or try differently next time? (Thoughtfully answer these questions in the space below. Use a separate sheet of paper if necessary to complete your reflection.)

Name: _____

Date: _____

Handout 22A: Informative/Explanatory Writing Checklist

Directions: Use this checklist to revise your writing. Mark + for "yes" and Δ for "not yet." Ask someone (adult or peer) to evaluate your writing as well.

Reading and Listening Comprehension	Self +/Δ	Peer +/Δ	Teacher +/Δ
Describe at least three ways Sal and Phoebe are connected.			
Include the main connection between Sal and Phoebe.			
Include related ideas shared in a class discussion.			
Structure			
I respond to all parts of the prompt.			
I focus on my topic throughout the paragraph.			
I introduce the topic clearly.			
I use at least three vocabulary words that are specific and appropriate to the content.			
My conclusion relates to my introduction.			
I use at least three linking words to connect ideas.			
Development			
I develop my topic with evidence from text(s).			
My evidence is related to the topic.			
I elaborate upon evidence by explaining or analyzing it.			
Style			
I use a variety of sentence patterns (simple, compound, complex).			
My writing style is appropriate for the audience.			

Writing Process			
I revise my essay to improve my ideas.			
I revise my essay to improve my word choice.			
I edit my essay for correct spelling.			
I edit my essay for correct punctuation.			
I edit my essay for correct capitalization.			
Total number of +'s			

Name: _____

Date: _____

Handout 23A: Fluency Homework

Directions:
1. Day 1: Read the text carefully and annotate to help you read fluently.
2. Each day:
   a. Practice reading the text aloud three to five times.
   b. Evaluate your progress by placing a checkmark in the appropriate, unshaded box.
   c. Ask someone (adult or peer) to listen and evaluate you as well.
3. Last day: Answer the self-reflection questions at the end.

I sat on the edge of a gorge in the Badlands, looking back at Gram and Gramps and the pregnant woman on the blanket. I pretended that it was my mother sitting there and she would still have the baby and everything would be the way it was supposed to be. And then I tried to imagine my mother sitting here on her trip out to Lewiston, Idaho. Did all the people on the bus get out and walk around with her or did she sit by herself, like I was doing? Did she sit here in this spot and did she see that pink spire? Was she thinking about me?

I picked up a flat stone and sailed it across the gorge where it hit the far wall and plummeted down, down, careening off the jagged outcroppings. My mother once told me the Blackfoot story of Napi, the Old Man who created men and women. To decide if these new people should live forever or die, Napi selected a stone. "If the stone floats," he said, "you will live forever. If it sinks, you will die." Napi dropped the stone into the water. It sank. People die.

"Why did Napi use a stone?" I asked. "Why not a leaf?"

My mother shrugged. "If you had been there, you could have made the rock float," she said. She was referring to my habit of skipping stones across the water.

I picked up another rock and sailed it across the gorge, and this one, too, hit the opposite wall and fell down and down and down. It was not a river. It was a hole. What did I expect?

Creech, Sharon. *Walk Two Moons*. 1994. HarperCollins, 2011.

Student Performance Checklist:	Day 1		Day 2		Day 3		Day 4	
	You	Listener*	You	Listener*	You	Listener*	You	Listener*
Accurately read the passage three to five times.								
Read with appropriate phrasing and pausing.								
Read with appropriate expression.								
Read articulately at a good pace, and an audible volume.								

*Adult or peer

Self-reflection: What choices did you make when deciding how to read this passage, and why? What would you like to improve on or try differently next time? (Thoughtfully answer these questions in the space below. Use a separate sheet of paper if necessary to complete your reflection.)

Name: _____

Date: _____

Handout 24A: Story within a Story Map, Part 2

Directions: Record the main events under each category of each story in *Walk Two Moons*.

Sal's Memories of Kentucky	Phoebe's Story in Ohio	Sal's Journey to Idaho

Sal's Memories of Kentucky	Phoebe's Story in Ohio	Sal's Journey to Idaho

Sal's Return to Kentucky

Name: _____

Date: _____

Handout 25A: Poems in *Walk Two Moons*

Part 1

Directions: Read the poem, take notes in your Response Journal, and be prepared to discuss.

"the little horse is newlY"
by e.e. cummings

Born)he knows nothing,and feels
everything;all around whom is

perfectly a strange
ness(Of sun
light and of

fragrance and of Singing)is ev
erywhere(a welcom
ing dream:is amazing)
a worlD.and in

this world lies:smoothbeautifuL
ly folded;a(brea
thing a gro

Wing)silence,who; is:somE
oNe

Part 2

Directions: Follow along as you listen to a reading of the poem. Answer the questions on Handout 25B, rereading the poem as necessary.

"The Tide Rises, The Tide Falls"
by Henry Wadsworth Longfellow

The tide rises, the tide falls,
The twilight darkens, the curlew calls;
Along the sea-sands damp and brown
The traveler hastens toward the town,
        And the tide rises, the tide falls.

Darkness settles on roofs and walls,
But the sea, the sea in darkness calls;
The little waves, with their soft, white hands
Efface the footprints in the sands,
        And the tide rises, the tide falls.

The morning breaks; the steeds in their stalls
Stamp and neigh, as the hostler calls;
The day returns, but nevermore
Returns the traveler to the shore.
        And the tide rises, the tide falls

Name: _____

Date: _____

Handout 25B: "The Tide Rises, The Tide Falls"

Directions: Listen to the poem, read what Sal says about it on pages 169–170, and answer the questions together with your group. Cite from the text in some of your responses.

1. What mood does this poem have? How does hearing the poem add to the mood? What else do you notice about how the poem sounds?

_____

_____

_____

_____

2. What does Sal say about this poem? How does she say the poem makes her and Phoebe feel?

_____

_____

_____

_____

3. How does Sal summarize the poem? Cite from the text in your response. What do she and Phoebe think happens to the traveler?

_____

_____

_____

4. Why do you think the author includes this poem? How is the poem connected to the themes in this story?

_____

_____

_____

5. What do you think Ben means by "maybe dying could be normal and terrible"? (173) How does this connect back to the Blackfoot myth about Napi?

_____

_____

_____

Name:

Date:

Handout 25C: Themes/Messages/Lessons

Directions: Record the themes, messages on the porch, and lessons in *Walk Two Moons* in each box.

Themes

Messages on Phoebe's Porch	Message Meanings

Lessons

Name: _____

Date: _____

Handout 26A: Evidence Organizer for Focusing Question Task 4

Directions: Choose the best evidence from *Walk Two Moons* to support your focus statement. Write brief notes in the boxes. Remember to only write notes that support your focus statement.

Prompt: What does Sal learn in *Walk Two Moons*?

Focus Statement: Through her experiences and the messages on Phoebe's porch, Sal learns many things about herself, others, and the world in *Walk Two Moons*.

Context	Evidence	Source	Elaboration/Explanation
Is this lesson about self, others, and/or the world?	List details from the text that support your focus statement. Be sure to use quotations and paraphrasing.	Where did you find this information? List chapter and page number.	Give more information about the evidence and how it is connected to the messages on the porch.

Name:

Date:

Context	Evidence	Source	Elaboration/Explanation
Is this lesson about self, others, and/or the world?	List details from the text that support your focus statement. Be sure to use quotations and paraphrasing.	Where did you find this information? List chapter and page number.	Give more information about the evidence and how it is connected to the messages on the porch.

Name:

Date:

Handout 27A: Formal vs. Informal English

Directions: Read the following quotations from *Walk Two Moons*. The first set of quotations is written in informal English, and the second set of quotations is written in formal English. As you read, consider how informal English differs from formal English.

Informal English:

"Gramps barreled through Wyoming like a house afire. We snaked through winding roads where the trees leaned close, rustling *rush, rush, rush, rush, rush*." (193)

"'Huzza, huzza!' Gram said..." (193)

"'We had a wing-ding of an argument over it. You told me you had no dang idea how it got there.'" (194)

"'You've sure got your heart set on that, don't you, you stubborn gooseberry?' said Gramps." (209)

"'We're gonna eat up Montana,' Gramps said. 'We're gonna get to the I-dee-ho border tonight. You watch me. I'm putting this pedal to the metal—'" (212)

Formal English:

"It was late when we arrived at Yellowstone." (193)

"We parked the car and walked up a low hill." (210)

"There were people speaking languages other than English; next to us was a tour group of Italians; across the way was a group of Germans." (210–211)

What characteristics do you notice about formal vs. informal English? List those characteristics below in the table.

Formal	Informal

Sentences from *Walk Two Moons* by Sharon Creech.

Name: _____

Date: _____

Handout 28A: Fluency Homework

Directions:

1. Day 1: Read the text carefully and annotate to help you read fluently.
2. Each day:
   a. Practice reading the text aloud three to five times.
   b. Evaluate your progress by placing a check mark in the appropriate, unshaded box.
   c. Ask someone (adult or peer) to listen and evaluate you as well.
3. Last day: Answer the self-reflection questions at the end.

But as I sat there thinking these things, it occurred to me that a person couldn't stay all locked up in the house like Phoebe and her mother had tried to do at first. A person had to go and do things and see things, and I wondered, for the first time, if this had something to do with Gram and Gramps taking me on this trip.

The beagle in my lap was just like our Moody Blue. I rubbed her head and prayed for Gram. I thought about Moody Blue's litter of puppies. For the first week, Moody Blue wouldn't let anyone come anywhere near those puppies. She licked them clean and nuzzled them. They squealed and pawed their way up to her with their eyes still sealed.

Gradually, Moody Blue let us touch the puppies, but she kept her sharp eyes on us, and if we tried to take a puppy out of her sight, she growled. Within a few weeks, the puppies were stumbling away from her, and Moody Blue spent her days herding them back, but when they were about six weeks old, Moody Blue started ignoring them. She snapped at them and pushed them away. I told my mother that Moody Blue was being terrible. "She hates her puppies."

"It's not terrible," my mother said. "It's normal. She's weaning them from her."

"Does she have to do that? Why can't they stay with her?"

"It isn't good for her or for them. They have to become independent. What if something happened to Moody Blue? They wouldn't know how to survive without her."

While I prayed for Gram outside the hospital, I wondered if my mother's trip to Idaho was like Moody Blue's behavior. Maybe part of it was for my mother and part of it was for me.

Creech, Sharon. *Walk Two Moons*. 1994. HarperCollins, 2011.

Student Performance Checklist:	Day 1		Day 2		Day 3		Day 4	
	You	Listener*	You	Listener*	You	Listener*	You	Listener*
Accurately read the passage three to five times.								
Read with appropriate phrasing and pausing.								
Read with appropriate expression.								
Read articulately at a good pace, and an audible volume.								

*Adult or peer

Self-reflection: What choices did you make when deciding how to read this passage, and why? What would you like to improve on or try differently next time? (Thoughtfully answer these questions in the space below. Use a separate sheet of paper if necessary to complete your reflection.)

Name: _____

Date: _____

Handout 28B: Frederick/Fredericka and Freddy/Franny

Directions: Draw in facial features on each "face" for Formal Frederick/Fredericka and Informal Freddy/Franny, adding features for each that are fitting. Then, fold the paper in half and use each side for the lesson activity where you flip to the correct person who is speaking—Formal Frederick/Fredericka or Informal Freddy/Franny.

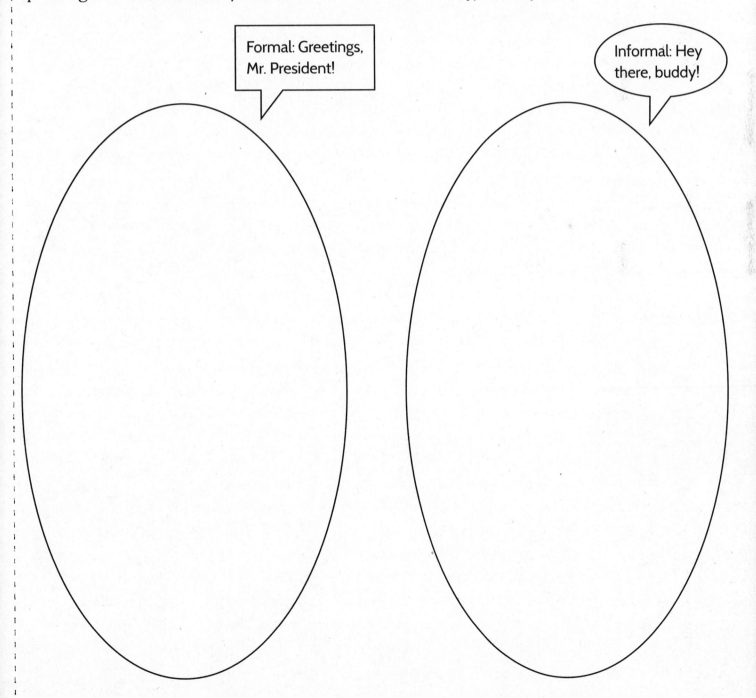

Name: _____

Date: _____

Handout 30A: Norms for Speaking Collaboratively

Directions: Read these instructions together with your class to prepare for discussion.

What does it mean to *speak collaboratively*?

To *speak collaboratively* means to engage with peers in an academic conversation to meet a common goal.

When you *speak collaboratively* you work with others to share and respond to ideas in order to reach a greater understanding of a text or question.

Norms for speaking collaboratively

1. *Take turns speaking one at a time.* Speak at least once!

2. *Listen respectfully and carefully to others' ideas.* Give your full attention towards the person speaking.

3. *Build on the ideas of others.* Connect to what has been said and add related ideas.

4. *Ask questions.* Don't stay confused!

5. *Agree or disagree with ideas, not people.* Be polite!

6. *Ask others to support their ideas.* Ask for an example or evidence from the text.

7. *Invite new voices to share ideas.* Encourage other students to enter the conversation.

8. *Stay focused on the goal or question.* Do your part to help the group reach greater understanding of a text or question.

Name: _____

Date: _____

Handout 30B: Ways to Participate in a Collaborative Conversation

Directions: Choose and cut out one or two cards to use in the class discussion.

Make a connection between ideas. • *That idea relates back to...*	Explain your thinking. • *I think that because...*
Add on to what someone else says. • *I agree with _____, and I'd like to add...* • *I really like that idea because...*	Offer an example to support your own or someone else's idea. • *An example of that would be...*
Give a different viewpoint. • *I politely disagree with _____ because...* • *That's a great point, but I think...*	Ask a question or clarifying someone else's idea. • *I have a question about...* • *In other words, are you saying...?* • *_____, could you please rephrase that?*
Refocus the conversation on the question or purpose. • *I'd like to go back to what _____ was saying about...* • *Let's go back to the question/idea that...*	Elaborate on an idea to explain why it is important. • *That idea is important because...*
Encourage someone to tell more about their ideas. • *That's an interesting idea. Can you say more about that?*	Summarize the conversation. • *So, the big idea seems to be...* • *So, what can we conclude from this?*

Name: _____

Date: _____

Handout 31A: Informative/Explanatory Writing Checklist

Directions: Use this checklist to revise your writing. Mark **+** for "yes" and Δ for "not yet." Ask someone (adult or peer) to evaluate your writing as well.

Reading Comprehension	Self +/Δ	Peer +/Δ	Teacher +/Δ
Describe two main lessons Salamanca learns.			
Explain one message and how it connects to Sal's first lesson.			
Explain another message and how it connects to Sal's second lesson.			
Optional: Connect a lesson from "Pandora's Box" to Sal.			
Structure			
I respond to all parts of the prompt.			
I focus on my topic throughout the piece.			
I introduce the topic clearly in my introduction paragraph.			
I organize my ideas into body paragraphs.			
My conclusion paragraph restates my focus statement and gives the reader something to reflect about.			
I use transitions to link paragraphs and ideas.			
Development			
I develop my topic with evidence from text(s).			
My evidence is related to the topic.			
I elaborate upon evidence by explaining or analyzing it.			
Style			
I use a variety of sentence patterns (simple, compound, complex).			

I use vocabulary words that are specific and appropriate to the content.			
My writing style is appropriate for the audience.			
Writing Process			
I revise my essay to improve my ideas.			
I revise my essay to improve my word choice.			
I edit my essay for correct spelling.			
I edit my essay for correct punctuation.			
I edit my essay for correct capitalization.			
Total number of +'s			

Name: _____

Date: _____

Handout 32A: Evidence Organizer for End-of-Module Task

Directions: Choose the best evidence to support your focus statement. Write brief notes in the boxes. Follow the prompts at the top of the chart. Remember to only write notes that support your focus statement.

Prompt: What can we learn from myths and stories?

Focus Statement:

Context	Evidence	Source	Elaboration/Explanation
Themes in myths? What are the lessons we can learn?	List details from the text that support your focus statement. Be sure to use quotations and paraphrasing.	Where did this information come from? List title and page number.	Why is this important? What does this help us understand?

Prompt: What can we learn from myths and stories?

Focus Statement:

Context	Evidence	Source	Elaboration/Explanation
Themes in myths? What are the lessons we can learn?	List details from the text that support your focus statement. Be sure to use quotations and paraphrasing.	Where did this information come from? List title and page number.	Why is this important? What does this help us understand?

Name: _____

Date: _____

Handout 33A: Speaking and Listening Checklist

Directions: Evaluate your participation by marking + for "yes" and Δ for "not yet" in the appropriate boxes. Ask someone (adult or peer) to evaluate your participation as well.

	Self +/Δ	Peer +/Δ	Teacher +/Δ
I followed all the rules for speaking in a group.			
I listened respectfully and carefully to my peers' ideas.			
I spoke clearly and at an understandable pace.			
I paraphrased what I heard my peers say before adding my own comments.			
I made comments that contributed to discussion and greater understanding of the text(s) or question.			
My comments showed that I am engaged in and curious about what we are learning.			
I built and elaborated on comments from my peers.			
I supported my ideas with text evidence.			
I agreed and disagreed respectfully.			
I helped my peers stay focused on the goal or question.			
Total number of +'s			

Name: _____

Date: _____

Handout 34A: End-of-Module Task Essay Planner

Directions: Use this planner to help you develop and organize your ideas for your End-of-Module Task.

Introduction

Hook (H) red	How will you "hook" your audience, or catch their attention?
Introduce (I) red	Introduce your topic. Provide any necessary background information or context for your topic.
Thesis (T) green	State your essential idea about what we can learn from myths and stories, previewing your two supporting points (i.e., two big ideas we learn from reading myths and stories).

	Point 1– (first idea we learn)	Point 2– (second idea we learn)

Supporting Paragraph 1–Point 1: _____

Topic Statement (To S) yellow	State your first point in support of your thesis.
Evidence (E) yellow	Cite evidence from the module texts that develops point 1, including any necessary context:
Elaboration (E) yellow	Explain how the evidence develops point 1 and how it can impact people today:
Concluding Statement (C) yellow	Close your paragraph.

Name: _____

Date: _____

Supporting Paragraph 2—Point 2: _____

Topic Statement (To S) blue	Transition from your last point, and state your second point in support of your thesis.
Evidence (E) blue	Cite evidence from the module texts that develops point 2, including any necessary context:
Elaboration (E) blue	Explain how the evidence develops point 2 and how it can impact people today:
Concluding Statement (C) blue	Close your paragraph.

Conclusion

Conclusion (C) green	Reinforce your thesis.
	Reflect on the significance of your thesis. What do you want your reader to remember about the big ideas we can learn from reading myths and stories?

Name: _____

Date: _____

Handout 35A: Informative/Explanatory Writing Checklist

Directions: Use this checklist to revise your writing. Mark + for "yes" and Δ for "not yet." Ask someone (adult or peer) to evaluate your writing as well.

Reading Comprehension	Self +/Δ	Peer +/Δ	Teacher +/Δ
I describe one theme we can learn from myths and stories.			
I describe a second theme we can learn from myths and stories.			
I refer to text evidence to support your points.			
I explain why these themes matter.			
Structure			
I respond to all parts of the prompt.			
I focus on my topic throughout the piece.			
I introduce the topic clearly in my introduction paragraph.			
I provide background information in my introduction.			
I organize my ideas into body paragraphs.			
My conclusion paragraph relates to my thesis.			
I use transitions to link paragraphs and ideas.			
Development			
I develop my topic with evidence from texts.			
My evidence is related to the topic.			
I elaborate upon evidence by explaining how it supports my thesis.			

Style			
I use a variety of sentence patterns (simple, compound, complex).			
I use three vocabulary words that are specific and appropriate to the content. Circle them.			
My writing style is appropriate for the audience.			
Conventions			
I use two modal auxiliaries (can, may, must). Underline them.			
Writing Process			
I revise my essay to improve my ideas.			
I revise my essay to improve my word choice.			
I edit my essay for correct spelling.			
I edit my essay for correct punctuation.			
I edit my essay for correct capitalization.			
Total number of +'s			

Name: _____

Date: _____

Handout 36A: Greatest Heart Nominee

Directions for the Awards Skit:

- Select a passage from your text which provides the evidence for your character's Great Heart. Use the fluency checklist on the bottom of this handout to decide when your reading is fluent.

- Create a precise name for your nominees' Great Heart Award (e.g. The Hopeful Great Heart Award, The Selfless Great Heart Award).

- Generate a list of reasons why your nominee won this Great Heart Award.

- Using items cut from magazines or printed from a computer, create a specialized poster award that would be meaningful to your character or person. You may also draw your own images, or use a multimedia program like Slideshow or Prezi to create the award.

- Write an acceptance speech for your nominee (character) which includes the following success criteria:

  - Use two vocabulary words from this module.
  - Use two transition words or phrases.
  - Use one reference to a myth from Module 4.

- Practice presenting your award.

  - Assign one group member to introduce your character by reading the text passage from your real or imagined character.
  - Assign one group member to present the award.
  - Assign one group member to role play the real or imagined character and read the acceptance speech.

Fluency Checklist:

Student Performance Checklist:	Reading One		Reading Two		Reading Three	
	You	Listener	You	Listener	You	Listener
Read with appropriate phrasing and pausing.						
Read with appropriate expression.						
Read articulately at a good pace and an audible volume.						

Volume of Reading Reflection Questions

Myth Making, Grade 4, Module 4

Student Name: _____

Text: _____

Author: _____

Topic: _____

Genre/type of book: _____

Directions: Share what you have learned through reading.

Informational Text:

1. Wonder: Study the cover, the back, and the table of contents. Tapping your honest curiosity, write three questions that stem from the information.

2. Organize: Choose one rich paragraph in the text. Retell the paragraph in your own words, either in writing or orally.

3. Reveal: Consider how this text is structured. Is it organized by chronology (sequence), comparison, cause/effect, or problem/solution? How does knowing the structure help you to understand the information in the text?

4. Distill: What is the essential meaning of this text? What is communicated by the author's choice of topics?

5. Know: How did this text build your knowledge? Explain how the information you learned in this text built your knowledge from other texts. Connect the information between the two with specific examples.

6. Vocabulary: Write three important vocabulary words and define them as best you can from the context clues. Look each word up in a dictionary to check your definition. Be sure to choose the definition that makes sense in the passage.

Literary Text

1. Wonder: What about the front and/or back covers makes you curious? Jot down three questions you have about this story before you begin to read.

2. Organize: Summarize this story. Use the most helpful summary idea you learned this year.

3. Reveal: Choose the most exciting part of this story. If you were a movie director or screen writer, how would you stage this part of the story? What would you say to the actors as they portray the characters in this scene?

4. Distill: What is a theme of this story? Provide evidence from the text to support your response. How is this theme similar to other stories you have read this year? Does it relate to any of the mythology themes you have studied? How?

5. Know: How does this story build on what you have already learned about mythology?

6. Vocabulary: Look for two key words or phrases in this book that are intended as figurative language or related to mythology. Write a sentence for each word or phrase, that shows you understand the word or phrase.

WIT & WISDOM PARENT TIP SHEET

WHAT IS MY GRADE 4 STUDENT LEARNING IN MODULE 4?

Wit & Wisdom is our English curriculum. It builds knowledge of key topics in history, science, and literature through the study of excellent texts. By reading and responding to stories and nonfiction texts, we will build knowledge of the following topics:

Module 1: A Great Heart

Module 2: Extreme Settings

Module 3: The Redcoats Are Coming!

Module 4: Myth Making

In the fourth module, *Myth Making*, we will read and analyze myths from the ancient Greeks and Romans, as well as Native American tribes, to learn the purpose and importance of these stories in their cultures. Students will also enjoy reading *Walk Two Moons*, a beautiful tapestry of stories within stories to reveal a modern-day myth that captures a snapshot of our human experience. We will ask the question: *What can we learn from myths and stories?*

OUR CLASS WILL READ THESE BOOKS:

Novel (Literary)

- *Walk Two Moons*, Sharon Creech

Drama (Literary)

- *Pushing Up the Sky: Native American Plays for Children*, Joseph Bruchac

Historical Account (Informational)

- *Understanding Greek Myths*, Natalie Hyde

Myths (Literary)

- *Gifts from the Gods: Ancient Words & Wisdom from Greek & Roman Mythology*, Lise Lunge-Larsen

OUR CLASS WILL EXAMINE THESE PAINTINGS:

- *Pandora*, Dante Gabriel Rossetti
- *Pandora*, Odilon Redon

OUR CLASS WILL EXAMINE THIS GRAPHIC:

- "The Raven Steals the Light," Bill Reid and Robert Bringhurst

OUR CLASS WILL READ THIS MYTH:

- "When Raven Soared," Leigh Anderson

OUR CLASS WILL READ THESE POEMS:

- "The Tide Rises, The Tide Falls," Henry Wadsworth Longfellow
- "the little horse is newlY," e.e. cummings

OUR CLASS WILL EXAMINE THIS SCULPTURE:

- *Winged Victory of Samothrace*

OUR CLASS WILL WATCH THESE VIDEOS:

- "Aerial Acropolis focusing on Parthenon house of goddess Athena/Acropolis, Athens, Greece"
- "Secrets of the Parthenon," PBS *Nova*
- "The Tide Rises, The Tide Falls"
- "Samothrace Reconstruction: Hieron to Nike"

OUR CLASS WILL VIEW THIS PHOTOGRAPH:

- *Parthenon*, Britannica

OUR CLASS WILL ASK THESE QUESTIONS:

- What are myths, and why do people create them?
- What do myths and stories from different cultures have in common?
- How are Sal's and Phoebe's stories connected in *Walk Two Moons*?
- What does Sal learn in *Walk Two Moons*?

QUESTIONS TO ASK AT HOME:

As your Grade 4 Student reads, ask:

- How does this text build your knowledge of myths and stories? Share what you know about myths and stories.

BOOKS TO READ AT HOME:

- *Treasury of Egyptian Mythology: Classic Stories of Gods, Goddesses, Monsters, & Mortals*, Donna Jo Napoli
- *Treasury of Greek Mythology: Classic Stories of Gods, Goddesses, Heroes, and Monsters*, Donna Jo Napoli
- *Pegasus*, Marianne Mayer
- *Cupid and Psyche*, M. Charlotte Craft
- *A Collection of Rudyard Kipling's Just So Stories*, Rudyard Kipling
- *Greek Myths for Young Children*, Heather Amery
- *Percy Jackson and the Olympians: The Lightning Thief*, Rick Riordan
- *Fables*, Arnold Lobel
- *The Water Dragon: A Chinese Legend*, Li Jian
- *Classic Myths to Read Aloud: The Great Stories of Greek and Roman Mythology*, William F. Russell

IDEAS FOR TALKING ABOUT MYTHS AND STORIES:

- Ask your Grade 4 student to explain what makes a myth, a myth.
- Retell a myth and explain its purpose.
- Explain why people first created myths.
- Explain the two main types of myths.
- Discuss what the ancient Greeks learned from myths.
- Summarize what was happening in the books read in class.
- Create a comic strip story map to record in pictures what is happening in each story that is read in class. Discuss with your child each night.
- Practice reading aloud the fluency passages assigned for homework.
- Discuss the characters in *Walk Two Moons*. Who are they? Why are they important to the story?
- Discuss the trip Salamanca takes with her grandparents. Ask where they traveled to each day and look these places up together in books and on the internet.
- Write your own family myth and share it with others.

CREDITS

Great Minds® has made every effort to obtain permission for the reprinting of all copyrighted material. If any owner of copyrighted material is not acknowledged herein, please contact Great Minds® for proper acknowledgment in all future editions and reprints of this module.

- All material from the *Common Core State Standards for English Language Arts & Literacy in History/Social Studies, Science, and Technical Subjects* © Copyright 2010 National Governors Association Center for Best Practices and Council of Chief State School Officers. All rights reserved.

- All images are used under license from Shutterstock.com unless otherwise noted.

- The Painted Essay® is used by permission of Diana Leddy.

- Handout 12B: "The Sun, Moon, and Stars" retold by Donna Henes from *Around and About the Planets*, Appleseeds January 2007. Text copyright © 2007 by Carus Publishing Company. Reprinted by permission of Cricket Media. All Cricket Media material is copyrighted by Carus Publishing d/b/a Cricket Media, and/or various authors and illustrators. Any commercial use or distribution of material without permission is strictly prohibited. Please visit **http://www.cricketmedia.com/info/licensing2** for licensing and **http://www.cricketmedia.com** for subscriptions.

- Handout 12B: "Legend of the Moccasin Flower: An Ojibwe Tale" retold by Mary Morton Cowan from Faces magazine April 2010. Text copyright © 2010 by Carus Publishing Company. Reprinted by permission of Cricket Media. All Cricket Media material is copyrighted by Carus Publishing d/b/a Cricket Media, and/or various authors and illustrators. Any commercial use or distribution of material without permission is strictly prohibited. Please visit **http://www.cricketmedia.com/info/licensing2** for licensing and **http://www.cricketmedia.com** for subscriptions.

- Handout 14A: "When Raven Soared" by Leigh Anderson from *What a Story! Myths and More*, Appleseeds March 2008. Text copyright © 2008 by Carus Publishing Company. Reprinted by permission of Cricket Media. All Cricket Media material is copyrighted by Carus Publishing d/b/a Cricket Media, and/or various authors and illustrators. Any commercial use or distribution of material without permission is strictly prohibited. Please visit **http://www.cricketmedia.com/info/licensing2** for licensing and **http://www.cricketmedia.com** for subscriptions.

- For updated credit information, please visit **http://witeng.link/credits**.

ACKNOWLEDGMENTS

Great Minds® Staff

The following writers, editors, reviewers, and support staff contributed to the development of this curriculum.

Ann Brigham, Lauren Chapalee, Sara Clarke, Emily Climer, Lorraine Griffith, Emily Gula, Sarah Henchey, Trish Huerster, Stephanie Kane-Mainier, Lior Klirs, Liz Manolis, Andrea Minich, Lynne Munson, Marya Myers, Rachel Rooney, Aaron Schifrin, Danielle Shylit, Rachel Stack, Sarah Turnage, Michelle Warner, Amy Wierzbicki, Margaret Wilson, and Sarah Woodard.

Colleagues and Contributors

We are grateful for the many educators, writers, and subject-matter experts who made this program possible.

David Abel, Robin Agurkis, Elizabeth Bailey, Julianne Barto, Amy Benjamin, Andrew Biemiller, Charlotte Boucher, Sheila Byrd-Carmichael, Eric Carey, Jessica Carloni, Janine Cody, Rebecca Cohen, Elaine Collins, Tequila Cornelious, Beverly Davis, Matt Davis, Thomas Easterling, Jeanette Edelstein, Kristy Ellis, Moira Clarkin Evans, Charles Fischer, Marty Gephart, Kath Gibbs, Natalie Goldstein, Christina Gonzalez, Mamie Goodson, Nora Graham, Lindsay Griffith, Brenna Haffner, Joanna Hawkins, Elizabeth Haydel, Steve Hettleman, Cara Hoppe, Ashley Hymel, Carol Jago, Jennifer Johnson, Mason Judy, Gail Kearns, Shelly Knupp, Sarah Kushner, Shannon Last, Suzanne Lauchaire, Diana Leddy, David Liben, Farren Liben, Jennifer Marin, Susannah Maynard, Cathy McGath, Emily McKean, Jane Miller, Rebecca Moore, Cathy Newton, Turi Nilsson, Julie Norris, Galemarie Ola, Michelle Palmieri, Meredith Phillips, Shilpa Raman, Tonya Romayne, Emmet Rosenfeld, Jennifer Ruppel, Mike Russoniello, Deborah Samley, Casey Schultz, Renee Simpson, Rebecca Sklepovich, Amelia Swabb, Kim Taylor, Vicki Taylor, Melissa Thomson, Lindsay Tomlinson, Melissa Vail, Keenan Walsh, Julia Wasson, Lynn Welch, Yvonne Guerrero Welch, Emily Whyte, Lynn Woods, and Rachel Zindler.

Early Adopters

The following early adopters provided invaluable insight and guidance for Wit & Wisdom:

- Bourbonnais School District 53 • Bourbonnais, IL
- Coney Island Prep Middle School • Brooklyn, NY
- Gate City Charter School for the Arts • Merrimack, NH
- Hebrew Academy for Special Children • Brooklyn, NY
- Paris Independent Schools • Paris, KY
- Saydel Community School District • Saydel, IA
- Strive Collegiate Academy • Nashville, TN
- Valiente College Preparatory Charter School • South Gate, CA
- Voyageur Academy • Detroit, MI

Design Direction provided by Alton Creative, Inc.

Project management support, production design, and copyediting services provided by ScribeConcepts.com

Copyediting services provided by Fine Lines Editing

Product management support provided by Sandhill Consulting